David
and
Goliath

and other Bible Stories

Retold by Vic Parker

Miles
KeLLy

First published in 2011 by Miles Kelly Publishing Ltd
Harding's Barn, Bardfield End Green, Thaxted, Essex, CM6 3PX, UK

2 4 6 8 10 9 7 5 3 1

EDITORIAL DIRECTOR *Belinda Gallagher*
ART DIRECTOR *Jo Cowan*
EDITOR *Carly Blake*
DESIGNERS *Michelle Cannatella, Joe Jones*
JUNIOR DESIGNER *Kayleigh Allen*
COVER DESIGNER *Joe Jones*
CONSULTANT *Janet Dyson*
PRODUCTION MANAGER *Elizabeth Collins*
REPROGRAPHICS *Stephan Davis, Ian Paulyn*

ISBN 978-1-84810-397-9

Printed in China

British Library Cataloguing-in-Publication Data
A catalogue record for this book is available from the British Library

ACKNOWLEDGEMENTS
The publishers would like to thank the following artists
who have contributed to this book:

The Bright Agency Katriona Chapman, Giuliano Ferri,
Mélanie Florian (inc. cover)

Advocate Art Alida Massari

*The publishers would like to thank Robert Willoughby and
the London School of Theology for their help in compiling this book.*

Made with paper from a sustainable forest

www.mileskelly.net   info@mileskelly.net

www.factsforprojects.com

Self-publish your
children's book

buddingpress.co.uk

Contents

Joshua and the Battle of Jericho

Moses returned from Mount Sinai with two new stone tablets on which God had again written the Ten Commandments. On God's command the Israelites built an ornate chest for the tablets to be kept in, which was called the Ark of the Covenant.

After many more years wandering in the wilderness, at last God thought the Israelites had earned the right to enter Canaan, the land he had long ago promised Abraham would be theirs.

The Israelites had to fight against the tribes in the lands around Canaan for many years. So many that Moses never got to enter the country that God had chosen for his people. When the time drew near that Moses realized he was going to die, he climbed up to a mountain-top and God showed him the Promised Land spread out far below. And so Moses died comforted, and a warrior called Joshua took over as ruler of the Israelites.

Then God told Joshua to be brave and bold. It was finally time to cross the River Jordan, which was all that remained to keep the Israelites from entering the Promised

Land. So Joshua told the people to prepare to fight. Meanwhile, he sent spies across the river into the city of Jericho to find out what they were up against. The spies were nearly discovered by soldiers because the king of Jericho had heard that enemies had entered the city. He sent troops to search for them, but a woman called Rahab helped the spies escape. In return, she asked for their promise that Joshua's army would not harm her family when they invaded, and the spies agreed. Joshua learnt about the city and the strength of the mighty walls that surrounded it. He drew up battle plans and prayed to God for help.

Then came the day when Joshua gathered the Israelites on the banks of the River Jordan and commanded everyone to

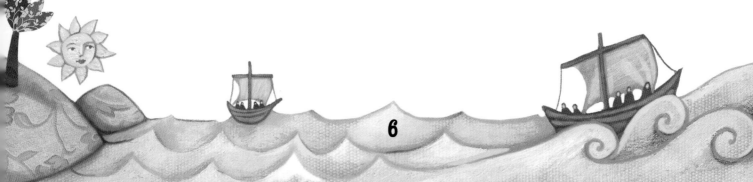

listen carefully. "As soon as the priests carrying the Ark of the Covenant at the front step into the river, the waters will stop flowing," Joshua announced. "As long as they stand holding the Ark in the river, we will all be able to cross safely."

To the Israelites' astonishment and joy, it happened exactly as their leader had said. Finally, Joshua's army of forty thousand men stood on a plain in the Promised Land.

The walls of the mighty city of Jericho were thick and high, and the city gates were barred against them. But Joshua listened to God, who told him exactly what to do.

Every day for six days, the Israelite army marched around the city walls. Behind the soldiers, priests with trumpets made of rams' horns carried the Ark of the Covenant.

For Jericho's people it was a terrifying and mysterious display of strength. What are the Israelites up to they wondered? Does that Ark really have magical powers? And why are they marching in that eerie silence? When will they attack?

Then on the seventh day the silence ceased and an almighty noise began.

Joshua gave the order for the priests to blow their horns for all they were worth as the army marched six times around the city walls.

As they began a seventh circuit, Joshua signalled for his soldiers to shout as loud as they could. Then such a roaring joined the blaring of the horns that the walls of Jericho trembled… and then shook… and then with a fearful rumble, collapsed to the ground.

Joshua's army entered the city and killed every man, woman and child they found there – all except for Rahab and her household, as she had been promised.

Deuteronomy chapter 34; Joshua chapters 1 to 6

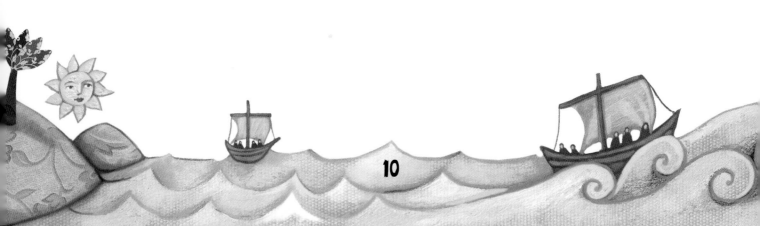

Samson the Strong

The Israelites suffered for many years at the hands of a people called the Philistines. However one day an angel appeared to an Israelite couple and gave a prediction: "You will have a son who will fight for Israel against the Philistines. You must raise him to worship God according to the strict rules of the Nazirite sect, and one

of these rules is that you must be careful never to cut his hair."

The couple were overjoyed when they did indeed have a baby boy. They called their little son Samson, but he didn't stay little for long. God ensured that Samson grew up to be tall and strong. He was so strong that once, when he was attacked by a lion, he killed it with his bare hands!

To his parents' immense dismay, Samson fell in love with a Philistine girl, and he insisted on marrying her.

At the wedding, Samson set his bride's guests a difficult riddle. They tried for three days to work it out but couldn't come up with the answer. In the end, they pestered the bride to find out, and she persuaded Samson to tell her so she could tell them. Samson realized what his new wife had done. In a temper, he killed thirty Philistines, and stormed off back home. By the time he calmed down and returned to reclaim his bride, she had married someone else!

Samson was so furious that he burned the Philistine harvest fields. When the Philistines found out why, they burned down the house of his former bride in turn. With this, Samson's rage knew no bounds and he single-handedly killed many more Philistines before he returned home.

From then on Samson was the Philistines' sworn enemy. They demanded that some Israelites from the tribe of Judah hand him over, or face the consequences. The men explained the situation to Samson, and Samson agreed to be bound and taken to his enemies. But once surrounded, he burst out of his ropes and attacked the Philistines, grabbing a nearby bone to use as a weapon. He left them all for dead before escaping.

Eventually the giant man became the leader of all Israel. He ruled for twenty years, but the Philistines never gave up

trying to capture him. Once, they waited until Samson was in the city of Gaza. They knew he would leave the next morning and planned to attack him by surprise at the city gates. But when they went there at dawn, they found that Samson had outsmarted them. He had left in the middle of the night, uprooting the massive, locked gates and carrying them off!

The Philistines saw yet another chance to take revenge on Samson when he fell in love with a woman called Delilah. Philistine chiefs visited Delilah and promised to pay her five thousand and five hundred pieces of silver if she handed him over to them. So each time Samson visited Delilah, she tested his great strength and tried to persuade him to tell her the secret of it. Eventually,

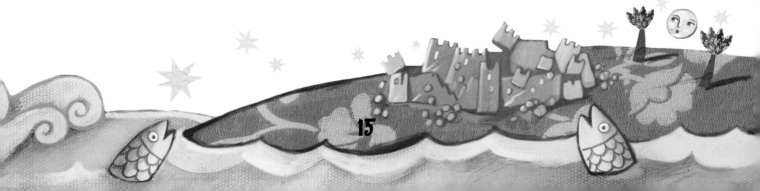

Samson gave in. "My parents promised God that I would never have my hair cut," he explained. "If I cut my hair, I lose God's protection and my strength will be gone."

Delilah's eyes lit up. At last, she knew! Next time Samson came to visit, she gave him wine and gradually he fell asleep. Then she cut off his hair and called the Philistines. It wasn't enough for Samson's enemies to bind him in chains, they blinded him too. Then they threw him in prison and set him to work as a slave.

Around a year passed, and the day came when the Philistines held a great festival in honour of their god, Dagon. The temple was so crowded that three thousand people spilled out onto the roof. There were prayers, songs, dances, poems and plays. Everyone enjoyed themselves immensely. Then people began shouting for Samson to be brought in, so they could mock the former great Israelite chief.

As the huge, blind man was led into the centre of the temple amid jeers, shouts and insults, no one thought anything of the fact that his hair had grown back. And as the crowd booed, hissed and cursed him, no one heard Samson pray, "Oh God, give me back my strength just one last

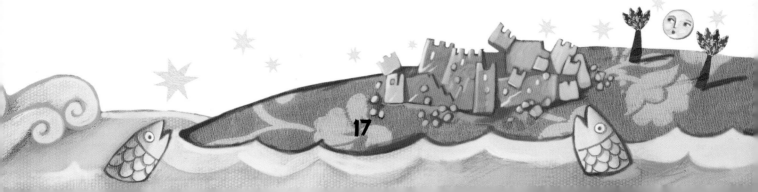

time." Samson stretched out his hands to his right and left and God helped him find the cold marble of the two main pillars of the temple. Then Samson gave a mighty roar. He pushed and heaved and strained. Amid screams and howls of terror, the huge pillars toppled apart and the temple crashed to the ground in ruins.

And so Samson died, taking many thousands of his enemies with him.

Judges chapters 13 to 16

Ruth the Loyal

Once, there was a terrible famine around Bethlehem. A starving man called Elimelech journeyed with his wife, Naomi, and two sons to live in Moab, where things were better. Then quite suddenly Elimelech died. Naomi and her sons were grief-stricken, but they tried to carry on as Elimelech would have wanted.

The boys married, Moabite girls called Ruth and Orpah. But then tragedy struck again – both boys died. Naomi was heartbroken.

"I am going to return home," Naomi told Ruth and Orpah, but Ruth refused to see the old, lonely widow go off on her own. "Where you go, I go," Ruth vowed. "Your people will be my people. Your god, my god."

Naomi smiled gratefully through her tears, and she and Ruth journeyed back to Bethlehem together.

Ruth and Naomi were now very poor. They struggled to make a living. One day, Ruth was in the fields at harvest time, collecting up the leftover corn when she caught the eye of the farm-owner, a man

called Boaz. He stopped and asked who she was. Boaz happened to be a cousin of Naomi's and he did what he could to help Ruth. Boaz told her she was welcome in his fields all the time. He told his harvesters to let her drink from their water jars whenever she wanted. He even invited Ruth to join his harvesters for a meal, giving her enough food to take home for supper. Boaz also secretly told his harvesters to leave extra corn behind so Ruth would have more to pick up.

Day after day, Boaz showed Ruth small kindnesses like these, and eventually Naomi dared to send Ruth to ask Boaz formally for his protection.

Boaz was delighted. As was tradition, he

went to the city gate and declared in public that he wanted to look after Ruth and Naomi. Boaz and Ruth were married, and Boaz cared for the women all their lives.

So Ruth was rewarded for her loyalty and kindness to Naomi, and Naomi was comforted in her old age. In the fullness of time, God sent Ruth a baby boy, Obed, who brought the two women happiness. They never dreamt that Obed would have a son called Jesse, who would have a son called David, who would one day become the greatest king Israel ever had.

Ruth chapters 1 to 4

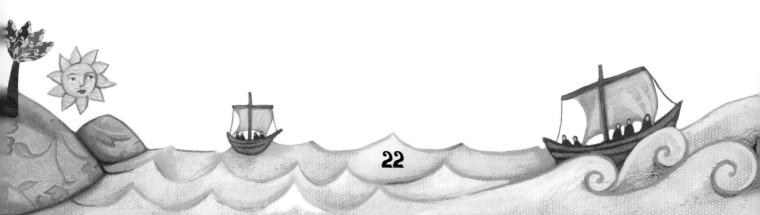

Samuel the Servant

Samuel was a little boy who lived with Eli, the high priest at the temple in Shiloh, where the Ark of the Covenant was kept. Samuel's mother Hannah had promised God that her son would serve Him all his life and learn how to be a priest one day.

Eli was a good man who looked after

Samuel lovingly. He had two sons of his own, but they grew up to be wicked and violent while Samuel was good and obedient.

One night, the little boy was woken by Eli calling his name. "Here I am!" Samuel called, and hurried to see what the high priest wanted.

"It wasn't me who called you," said Eli, quite confused. "Go back to bed, son."

But a while later, Samuel was again woken by Eli calling his name. "Here I am!" he cried again, and dashed off to find Eli.

"It wasn't me who called you!" Eli

reassured Samuel. "Now go back to bed, like a good boy."

But an hour or so later, the voice came again. "Samuel! Samuel!" And Samuel rushed off once more to Eli.

"Samuel," the old high priest said quietly, "I think it must be God who is calling you, and I think you're going to hear Him again. The next time it happens, don't come and find me. Instead call out, 'Speak, Lord, your servant is listening'."

Samuel went back and laid down on his bed in the darkness. And sure enough, the voice came again, "Samuel! Samuel!"

"Speak, Lord, your servant is listening," Samuel replied, just as Eli had told him.

God spoke to Samuel and gave him a difficult message to give the old high priest.

A day would come when God was going to punish Israel for its sins and Eli would be punished too, for his sons' wickedness.

In the morning, Samuel was afraid to tell Eli what God had said. When he finally did, the high priest wasn't angry with him. Instead, he hung his head in shame and sadness. "Let God do what He thinks is right," the old man said humbly.

That was the first of many messages that God gave Samuel. For Samuel grew up to be a great prophet who became the ruler of Israel, and was known throughout the land for always speaking the truth.

I Samuel chapters 1 to 3

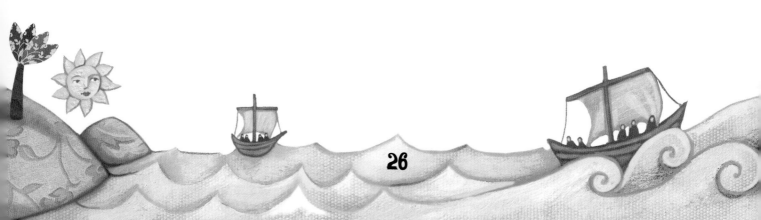

David and Goliath

The people of Israel saw that other nations had kings to rule them and demanded that they should have one too. The great prophet Samuel asked God for approval. He was told to choose a man called Saul from the tribe of Benjamin to be the first king of Israel.

King Saul won many victories against

Israel's enemies, but he did not always do as God wanted. For this reason, God told Samuel that Saul's sons would never be king. God ordered that Samuel travel to Bethlehem and find a shepherd boy called David, the youngest son of a man called Jesse. It was David that God wanted to be the next king. Samuel did so, and gave David a special blessing, and from then on God was always with him.

King Saul's army often had to fight the Philistines because they were constantly invading Israelite territory. Every Israelite who could be spared was called to defend their lands, and three of Jesse's other sons went to the frontline. One day, Jesse sent David off with food supplies for them. He reached the camp as a battle was beginning and the armoured soldiers were marching onto the battlefield. Suddenly, they all turned and came running back in fear.

"Whatever is going on?" David called as one terrified soldier ran past.

The man just shouted, "Look!" and pointed behind him.

Striding out in front of the Philistine army was a warrior more enormous than David could have dreamt. He was almost twice as big as everyone else!

"Run away if you like," the giant bellowed. "There's no need to do battle if you're

too cowardly. Just send someone to fight me in single combat. Whoever wins has victory for their side. Now, is any one of you men big enough to take up the challenge?" He smashed his mighty spear against his shield and threw back his head and roared, and the noise crashed around the surrounding hills like thunder.

David was outraged. "How dare he! It's an insult not just to us but to God!" he spat. "Just let me at him! Out in the pastures, I've killed lions and bears when they've attacked my father's flocks and I can do the same to this beast too! God protected me then as He will protect me now."

"Well…" said Saul, casting around for other volunteers. None were forthcoming. "Very well, and God be with you."

Saul insisted on dressing David in his own armour, but it was so big and bulky that he couldn't move, so David took it off again. He strode out to meet the giant, Goliath of Gath, with just his staff, his slingshot and five smooth stones in his shepherd's pouch.

King Saul and his army watched in amazement. The giant was roaring with laughter as a mere child walked towards him. The young boy was yelling back that he was going to slay Goliath in the name of God. The shepherd boy stood firm as the giant ran towards him with death in his eyes, brandishing his spear.

Then David raised his slingshot and whirled it around once… A stone struck Goliath in the forehead, sending him

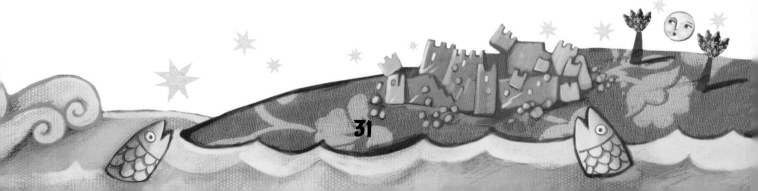

crashing to the ground, dead. As King Saul
and his army cheered, David drew the
giant's sword and cut off Goliath's head
with one blow.

And the Philistines
turned and fled, leaving
the Israelites triumphant.

I Samuel chapters 8, 9, 16, 17

Solomon the Wise

When Saul, the first king of Israel died, David came to the throne, just as God had wanted. It was King David who made Israel a great, unified nation with Jerusalem as its capital city. He had the Ark of the Covenant brought there amid great rejoicing. He wanted to build a glorious temple to house it, but God told David that

He was going to entrust that job to his son, Solomon, the third king of Israel.

Solomon was in his early twenties when he took over the throne. He was determined to carry on his father's good work, strengthening the nation and keeping peace with Israel's enemies, but he wasn't sure exactly how to do it. He felt he lacked the experience and confidence he needed to be a good king.

One night, God appeared to Solomon in a dream and asked how He could help. "Please, God, give me the gift of wisdom," the king begged.

God was delighted. Solomon could have asked God to give him gold or long life or power over his enemies, or a whole range of other selfish things. Wisdom to govern the

people well was an excellent choice and God was only too happy to oblige.

Not long afterwards, two women who were in the middle of a bitter argument were brought before Solomon so he could settle their dispute. The women lived together and both had recently given birth to a child. However, one of the babies had died, and now each woman was claiming the living baby as hers.

"It's her baby who died," the first one insisted to Solomon. "Do you think I don't know my own child?"

"No, her baby died!" the second woman protested. "Then she stole mine."

Solomon signalled for the women to be quiet. After a few minutes he announced, "Bring me my sword!" As the weapon was

fetched he continued, "Cut the child in two and give half to each woman!"

"Yes, neither of us should have him!" cried one woman.

But the other burst out wailing. "Sire, please! I would rather see him given away to her than for him to be hurt!"

Then Solomon knew who the real mother of the baby was. And all the people of Israel knew that such wisdom could only have come from God.

II Samuel chapters 5 to 7; I Kings chapters 1, 3

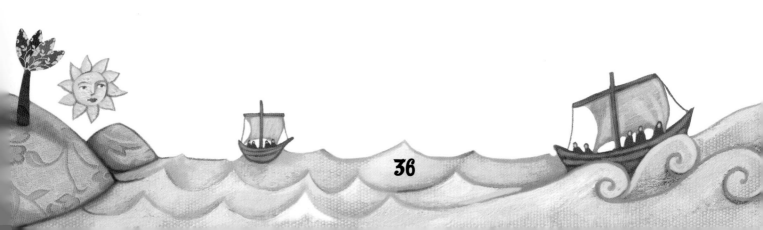

Solomon the Magnificent

The nation of Israel prospered under King Solomon. He kept peace in his lands and trading routes thrived as merchants could travel in safety. He ruled wisely and well, stunning everyone with his incredible knowledge. Then Solomon began to fulfil his father's dream of building a glorious temple, just as God had said he would. After nearly five hundred years, the Ark of the Covenant was to have a home.

Solomon drafted thousands of workers to build the temple. It was made from beautiful cedar wood, which came from the lands of a friend of his, King Hiram of Tyre in Lebanon. Solomon wanted to use only the finest materials and the newest, most exciting techniques, even if it meant going to great lengths and expense to bring materials and craftspeople from abroad. Labourers spent years building massive stone pillars, carving enormous doors and wooden wall panels with angels and intricate flowers, dying and weaving beautiful curtains, and lining whole rooms with gold, which were then decorated with stunning jewels.

The day finally came when Solomon ordered the temple to be filled with treasures and the Ark of the Covenant brought to its new home. It was done with such procession and celebrating that no one had ever seen anything like it. As the priests were leaving the temple, the building was suddenly filled with a blazing light so bright that no one could look at it. The king stood in front of the altar before all of his people and gave thanks to God, praying that He would always be with the nation of Israel. Then began a week of feasting.

Solomon didn't stop his building plans at the temple. He erected a magnificent palace and splendid buildings in Jerusalem and Canaan. Rulers from far-off countries travelled to see the marvels for themselves. Even the Queen of Sheba made a journey of fifteen hundred miles through the desert in a camel train laden down with spices, jewels and gold. The queen was amazed – not just by Solomon's incredible buildings but by the wisdom with which he ran the country. "Praise be to your God," she exclaimed, "for He must be hugely pleased with what you have done in His honour."

I Kings chapters 4 to 8, 10